# CONTENTS

G000295169

# THE ALPHABET

## THE ALPHABET

The alphabet is made up of vowels and consonants:

ALPHABET = VOWELS + CONSONANTS
(26 letters)　(5 letters)　(21 letters)

A B C D E F G H I J K L M N O P Q R S T U V W X Y Z

## VOWELS

A vowel is a **type of sound** for which there is no closure of the mouth at any point to stop the air when said. There are five letters in the alphabet that are vowels.

A E I O U
a e i o u

## CONSONANTS

Consonants **are sounds** for which there is at least one point where the air is stopped with the mouth, tongue or throat when said. There are 21 letters in the alphabet that are consonants:

_ B C D _ F G H _ J K L M N _ P Q R S T _ V W X Y Z
_ b c d _ f g h _ j k l m n _ p q r s t _ v w x y z

For more SKIPS titles visit our website.

# Chapter 1

# A PICTURE ALPHABET

 **A** a

 **B** b

 **C** c

 **D** d

 **E** e

 **F** f

 **G** g

**H** h

**I** i

 **J** j

 **K** k

**L** l

 **M** m

**N** n

 **O** o

 **P** p

**Q** q

 **R** r

 **S** s

 **T** t

 **U** u

 **V** v

 **W** w

 **X** x

 **Y** y

 **Z** z

# SHORT VOWEL SOUND: "a"

**All the words below contain the letter "a".**

Fill in the missing letters and copy the whole word into the CrossWord puzzle as shown.

## ACROSS →

1)  b a g

2)  t _ _

4) 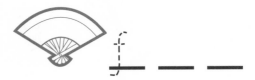 f _ _

6)  c _ _

7)  c _ _ b

10)  h _ _ _

11)  p _ _ m

## DOWN ↓

1)  b a t

3)  p _ _

5)  a _ _

6)  c l _ _ _

8)  b _ n _

9)  l _ m _

10)  h _ _

For more SKIPS titles visit our website.

"a" is a vowel

## SKIPS CHALLENGE TIME

Well done! Now copy the letters from the coloured tiles in the CrossWord to the matching coloured boxes below and **complete the sentence.**

**Remember:** boxes that are the same colour have the same letter in them.

The fat ▢▢▢

sat on a ▢▢▢

Place a SKIPS CHALLENGE sticker here

*Well done! It's SKIPS sticker time.*

# SHORT VOWEL SOUND: "e"

**All the words below contain the letter "e".**

Fill in the missing letters and copy the whole word into the CrossWord puzzle as shown.

| ACROSS → | DOWN ↓ |
|---|---|

**ACROSS →**

1)  p e n

3)  w _ _

5)  v _ _

6)  n _ s _

8)  h _ _

9)  s _ _ p

12)  L _ _

13)  b _ _

**DOWN ↓**

2)  n e t

3)  w _ _ L

4)  t _ _ t

5)  v _ s _

7)  t _ _

10)  p _ _

11)  r _ _

13)  b _ _ L

If you are not sure of the answer, simply move on and revisit once a few clues have been completed. **That's all part of the fun!**

For more SKIPS titles visit our website.

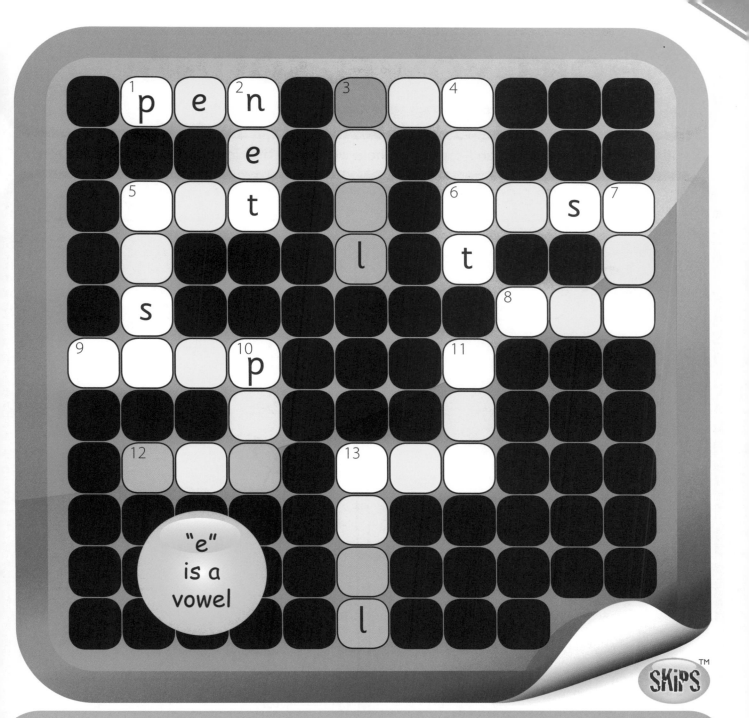

"e" is a vowel

## SKIPS CHALLENGE TIME

Well done! Now copy the letters from the coloured tiles in the CrossWord into the matching coloured boxes below and complete the sentence.

Remember: boxes that are the same colour have the same letter in them.

Peg ☐☐☐ fell

in a ☐☐☐☐

Place a SKIPS CHALLENGE sticker here

# SHORT VOWEL SOUND: "i"

**All the words below contain the letter "i".**

Fill in the missing letters and copy the whole word into the CrossWord puzzle as shown.

### ACROSS →

1)  L i p

3) 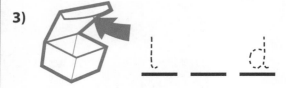 L _ d

5)  b _ _ _

7) 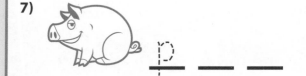 p _ _

9)  s _ n _

10) 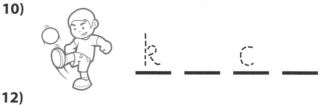 k _ c _

12)  s h _ _

14) 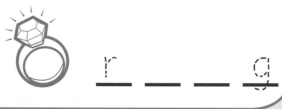 r _ _ g

### DOWN ↓

2) 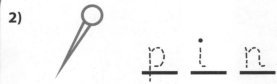 p i n

4)  d _ _ _

6)  i _ _ _

7)  p _ n _

8) 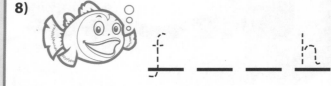 f _ _ h

11)  k _ n _

12) s _ _

13)  k _ _ s

If you are not sure of the answer, simply move on and revisit once a few clues have been completed. **That's all part of the fun!**

For more SKIPS titles visit our website.

Well done! Now copy the letters from the coloured tiles in the CrossWord into the matching coloured boxes below and complete the sentence.

Remember: boxes that are the same colour have the same letter in them.

Thin as a ▢▢▢

Jim wins a ▢▢▢

Place a SKIPS CHALLENGE sticker here

*Well done! It's SKIPS sticker time.*

**9**

www.skipscrosswords.co.uk

# SHORT VOWEL SOUND: "o"

**All the words below contain the letter "o".**

Fill in the missing letters and copy the whole word into the CrossWord puzzle as shown.

## ACROSS →

2)  h o p 

4)  f _ _

5)  c _ _

6)  d _ _

7)  s _ _ _

9)  l _ _ k

10)  l _ _

## DOWN ↓

1)  b o x

3)  p _ _

4)  f _ _ g

5)  c h _ _

6)  d _ _ l

7)  s _ _ k

8) 
bottom
t _ _

If you are not sure of the answer, simply move on and revisit once a few clues have been completed. **That's all part of the fun!**

For more SKIPS titles visit our website.

"o" is a vowel

## SKIPS CHALLENGE TIME

Well done! Now copy the letters from the coloured tiles in the CrossWord into the matching coloured boxes below and complete the sentence.

Remember: boxes that are the same colour have the same letter in them.

Is a ⬜⬜⬜⬜ a ⬜⬜⬜ or

is a ⬜⬜⬜ a spot?

Take your book to school and ask your teacher to put a

**WELL DONE SKIP!**

sticker here, and there's another sticker for you.

*Great! Show your teacher how well you've done.*

www.skipscrosswords.co.uk

# SHORT VOWEL SOUND: "u"

**All the words below contain the letter "u".**

Fill in the missing letters and copy the whole word into the CrossWord puzzle as shown.

## ACROSS →

2) 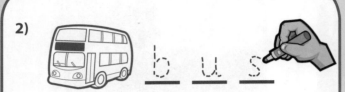 b u s

4)  g _ _

5) 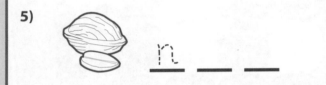 n _ _

7) 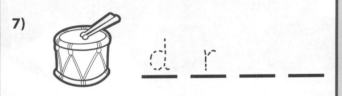 d r _ _

8)  b _ _ s h

## DOWN ↓

1) 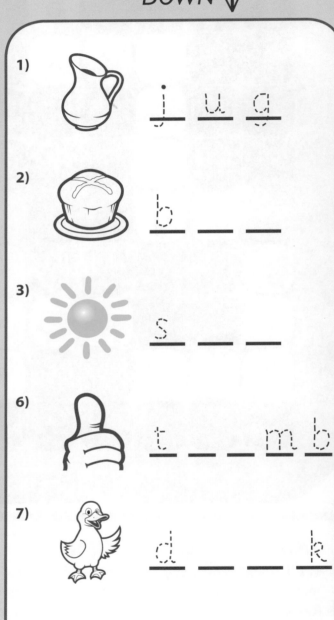 j u g

2) b _ _

3) s _ _

6) t _ _ m b

7) d _ _ k

If you are not sure of the answer, simply move on and revisit once a few clues have been completed. **That's all part of the fun!**

For more SKIPS titles visit our website.

## SKIPS CHALLENGE TIME

**Well done!** Now copy the letters from the coloured tiles in the CrossWord into the matching coloured boxes below and **complete the sentence.**

**Remember:** boxes that are the same colour have the same letter in them.

To eat a  in the  is fun!

Place a SKIPS CHALLENGE sticker here

Well done! It's SKIPS sticker time.

13

www.skipscrosswords.co.uk

# LONG SOUNDING: "a"

**For example:** a_e as in tape    ai as in rain    ay as in way

Fill in the missing letters and copy the whole word into the CrossWord puzzle as shown.

## ACROSS →

1)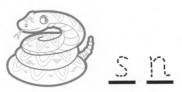
s n a k e

3)
g _ t _ _

5)
c _ k _

6)
L _ c _ _

8)
p l _ n _

10)
t _ _ _ y

## DOWN ↓

2)
n a i l

4)
t r _ _ n

7)
c h _ _ n

8)
p _ _ n t

9)
s a _ _ _

10)
t _ _ l

If you are not sure of the answer, simply move on and revisit once a few clues have been completed. **That's all part of the fun!**

For more SKIPS titles visit our website.

## SKIPS CHALLENGE TIME

Well done! Now copy the letters from the coloured tiles in the CrossWord into the matching coloured boxes below and complete the sentence.

Remember: boxes that are the same colour have the same letter in them.

# If your name starts with "A" you can

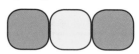 "Hooray!"

Place a SKIPS CHALLENGE sticker here

Well done! It's SKIPS sticker time.

15

www.skipscrosswords.co.uk

# LONG SOUNDING: "e"

**For example:** ea as in neat    ee as in keep    y as in tidy

Fill in the missing letters and copy the whole word into the CrossWord puzzle as shown.

## ACROSS →

2)
s e a

3)
e _ t

5)
w _ _ k

7)
l _ _ f

9)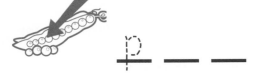
p _ _

11)
k _ _

## DOWN ↓

1)
b e e

2)
s h _ _ _

4)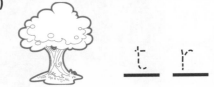
t r _ _ _

6)
k n _ _ _

8)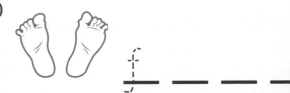
f _ _ _

10)
t h _ _ _

If you are not sure of the answer, simply move on and revisit once a
few clues have been completed. **That's all part of the fun!**

For more SKIPS titles visit our website.

You're doing great!

SKIPS

## SKIPS CHALLENGE TIME

Well done! Now copy the letters from the coloured tiles in the CrossWord into the matching coloured boxes below and complete the sentence.

Remember: boxes that are the same colour have the same letter in them.

# If your name starts with "E" then

Take your book to school and ask your teacher to put a **WELL DONE SKIP!** sticker here, and there's another sticker for you.

*Great! Show your teacher how well you've done.*

www.skipscrosswords.co.uk

# LONG SOUNDING: "i"

**For example:** i_e as in li<u>ne</u>    igh as in fight    y as in my

Fill in the missing letters and copy the whole word into the CrossWord puzzle as shown.

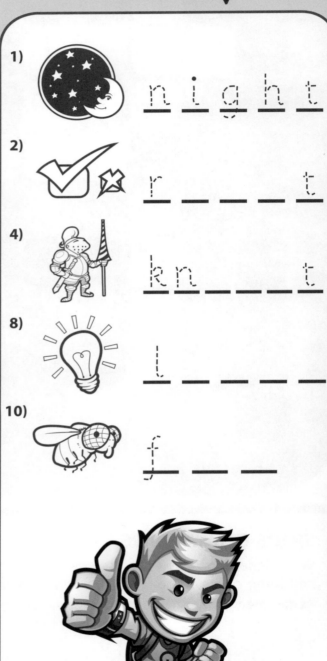

## ACROSS →

2) r i d e

3) b _ _ _

4) k _ _ _

5) t _ m _

6) n _ _ _

7) s m _ _ _

9) k n _ _ _

11) c r _ _

## DOWN ↓

1) n i g h t

2) r _ _ _ t

4) k n _ _ _ t

8) l _ _ _ _

10) f _ _ _

If you are not sure of the answer, simply move on and revisit once a few clues have been completed. **That's all part of the fun!**

For more SKIPS titles visit our website.

Well done, keep going!

ride
night

## SKIPS CHALLENGE TIME

**Well done!** Now copy the letters from the coloured tiles in the CrossWord into the matching coloured boxes below and **complete the sentence.**

**Remember:** boxes that are the same colour have the same letter in them.

If your name starts with "I" wink your ☐☐☐

Place a SKIPS CHALLENGE sticker here

*Well done! It's SKIPS sticker time.*

# LONG SOUNDING: "o"

**For example:** oa as in road     ow as in bow     o_e as in hope

Fill in the missing letters and copy the whole word into the CrossWord puzzle as shown.

ACROSS →

DOWN ↓

**2)**   b o a t

**3)**  l _ _ f

**4)**  c _ _ _ _

**6)**  g _ _ _

**9)**  t _ _ s t

**1)**  yellow

**2)**  b _ _ w

**5)**  t _ w

**7)** r _ _ _ _

**8)** b _ _ _

If you are not sure of the answer, simply move on and revisit once a few clues have been completed. **That's all part of the fun!**

## SKIPS CHALLENGE TIME

Well done! Now copy the letters from the coloured tiles in the CrossWord into the matching coloured boxes below and complete the sentence.

Remember: boxes that are the same colour have the same letter in them.

# If your name starts with "O"

## touch your ▢ ▢ ▢

Take your book to school and ask your teacher to put a **WELL DONE SKIP!** sticker here, and there's another sticker for you.

*Great! Show your teacher how well you've done.*

www.skipscrosswords.co.uk

# LONG SOUNDING: "u"

**For example:** u_e **as in** tu**b**e   ue **as in** arg**ue**   ew **as in** f**ew**

Fill in the missing letters and copy the whole word into the CrossWord puzzle as shown.

## ACROSS →

2)

m u s i c

4)

h _ g e

5)

c _ b e

7)

un_cor_

## DOWN ↓

1)

t u b e

3)

c _ _ _ w

6)

un_for_

If you are not sure of the answer, simply move on and revisit once a few clues have been completed. **That's all part of the fun!**

For more SKIPS titles visit our website.

## SKIPS CHALLENGE TIME

Well done! Now copy the letters from the coloured tiles in the CrossWord into the matching coloured boxes below and complete the sentence.

Remember: boxes that are the same colour have the same letter in them.

# If your name starts with "U"

say ⬜⬜⬜⬜⬜⬜⬜⬜ !

# CONSONANT BLENDS: "br"

**All the words below contain the letters "br".**

Fill in the missing letters and copy the whole word into the CrossWord puzzle as shown.

| ACROSS → | DOWN ↓ |
|---|---|

2)  b r o w n

1) 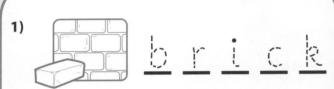 b r i c k

3)  b _ _ _ _

2)  b _ _ _ _

4)  b _ _ _ k

4)  b _ _ _ _

6)  b _ _ _ g _

5)  b _ _ _ _

7)  b _ _ _ _ _

sister

6) 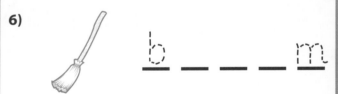 b _ _ _ m

If you are not sure of the answer, simply move on and revisit once a few clues have been completed. **That's all part of the fun!**

For more SKIPS titles visit our website.

# Chapter 2

Brilliant, brilliant, brilliant!

1 b    2 b r o w n
3      r
       i
       c    4              k
       k
                           5
6           g
                    7
m

SKIPS

## SKIPS CHALLENGE TIME

Well done! Now copy the letters from the coloured tiles in the CrossWord into the matching coloured boxes below and complete the sentence.

Remember: boxes that are the same colour have the same letter in them.

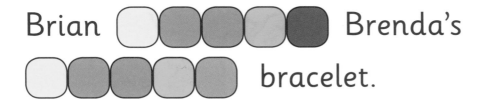

Brian ⬜⬜⬜⬜⬛ Brenda's

⬜⬜⬜⬜⬜ bracelet.

Place a SKIPS CHALLENGE sticker here

Well done! It's SKIPS sticker time.

# CONSONANT BLENDS: "ch"

**You will find the "<u>ch</u>" sound in all of these words.**

Fill in the missing letters and copy the whole word into the CrossWord puzzle as shown.

| ACROSS → | DOWN ↓ |
|---|---|

**ACROSS →**

1)   c h i n

2)  c _ _ _

5)  c _ _ _

7)  c _ _ _ _

9)  c _ _ _ _ _

10)  c _ _ _ _ _

**DOWN ↓**

1)  c a t c h

3)  p _ a _ _

4)  m _ _ _ _

6)  w _ t _ _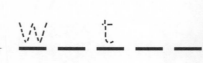

8)  t _ r _ _

If you are not sure of the answer, simply move on and revisit once a few clues have been completed. **That's all part of the fun!**

For more SKIPS titles visit our website.

**You're a champion CrossWord puzzler!**

## SKIPS CHALLENGE TIME

Well done! Now copy the letters from the coloured tiles in the CrossWord into the matching coloured boxes below and **complete the sentence.**

Remember: boxes that are the same colour have the same letter in them.

Should Chester ⬜⬜⬜⬜⬜⬜ the

shoes he ⬜⬜⬜⬜⬜ ?

Place a SKIPS CHALLENGE sticker here

Well done! It's SKIPS sticker time.

**27**

www.skipscrosswords.co.uk

# CONSONANT BLENDS: "sh"

**You will find the "sh" sound in all of these words.**

Fill in the missing letters and copy the whole word into the CrossWord puzzle as shown.

| ACROSS → | DOWN ↓ |
|---|---|

**ACROSS →**

2)   s h o e

4)  s _ _ _

5)  s _ _ _

7) 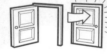 s _ _ t

9)  s _ _ _ _

12)  s _ _ r _

13)  s _ _ _ _

**DOWN ↓**

1)  f i s h

3)  h u _ _

6)  d _ _ _

8)  w _ _ _

10)  p _ _ _

11)  b _ _ _ _

If you are not sure of the answer, simply move on and revisit once a few clues have been completed. **That's all part of the fun!**

For more SKIPS titles visit our website.

Great work!

SKIPS™

## SKIPS CHALLENGE TIME

**Well done!** Now copy the letters from the coloured tiles in the CrossWord into the matching coloured boxes below and **complete the sentence.**

**Remember:** boxes that are the same colour have the same letter in them.

Shelley sells ☐☐☐☐☐☐ on

the ☐☐☐☐☐☐☐☐

Place a SKIPS CHALLENGE sticker here

# CONSONANT BLENDS: "st"

**All the words below contain the letters "st".**

Fill in the missing letters and copy the whole word into the CrossWord puzzle as shown.

## ACROSS →   DOWN ↓

4)  s t a r

5)  s _ _ _

6)  s t _ _

7) 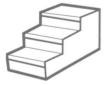 s _ _ _ k

11)  s _ a i r _

12)  s _ _ _ _

1)  v e s t

2)  e _ _ _

3)  p _ _ _ _

8)  c _ _ _ _

9)  g h _ _ _

10)  f _ _ _ _

If you are not sure of the answer, simply move on and revisit once a few clues have been completed. **That's all part of the fun!**

For more SKIPS titles visit our website.

Well done! Now copy the letters from the coloured tiles in the CrossWord into the matching coloured boxes below and **complete the sentence.**

Remember: boxes that are the same colour have the same letter in them.

Step by ☐☐☐☐ , let's go from

☐☐☐☐ to west.

Place a SKIPS CHALLENGE sticker here

*Well done! It's SKIPS sticker time.*

# DOUBLE LETTERS

**All the answers below contain letters that appear twice in a row.**

Fill in the missing letters and copy the whole word into the CrossWord puzzle as shown.

| ACROSS → | DOWN ↓ |
|---|---|

**ACROSS →**

2)  f e e t

4)  h _ _ l

5)  s _ _ _ p

8) 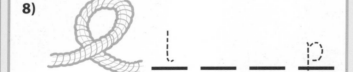 l _ _ p

10)  s t _ _ l

11)  d _ _ _ r

12)  b _ _ _ _ _

**DOWN ↓**

1) 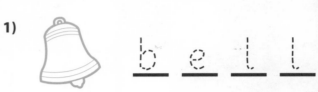 b e l l

2) 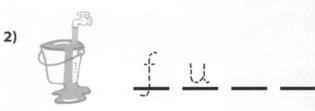 f u _ _

3) 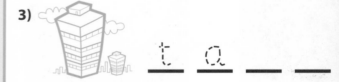 t a _ _ _

6) 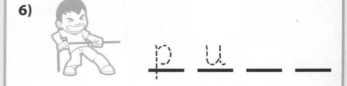 p u _ _ _

7)  l o _ _ y

9) 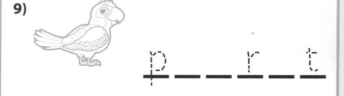 p _ _ r _ t

If you are not sure of the answer, simply move on and revisit once a few clues have been completed. **That's all part of the fun!**

For more SKIPS titles visit our website.

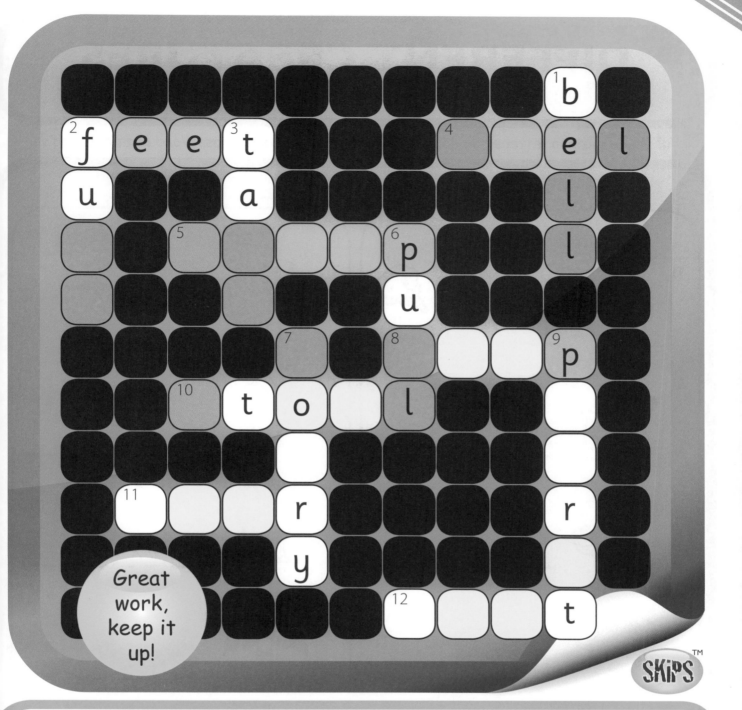

Great work, keep it up!

SKIPS

## SKIPS CHALLENGE TIME

Well done! Now copy the letters from the coloured tiles in the CrossWord into the matching coloured boxes below and complete the sentence.

Remember: boxes that are the same colour have the same letter in them.

Silly ▢▢▢▢▢ weep

and ▢▢▢▢▢

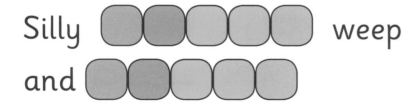

Take your book to school and ask your teacher to put a

**WELL DONE SKIP!**

sticker here, and there's another sticker for you.

*Great! Show your teacher how well you've done.*

# DIFFERENT CREATURES

**All the answers below are creatures.**

Fill in the missing letters and copy the whole word into the CrossWord puzzle as shown.

## ACROSS →

1)  c o w

3)  d _ _

5)  l _ _ _

6)  c _ _ _

8)  c _ _

11)  z _ _ _ _

## DOWN ↓

2)  o w l

3)  d _ _ _

4)  g _ _ _

7)  b _ _

9)  a _ _ _

10)  h _ _ _ _

If you are not sure of the answer, simply move on and revisit once a few clues have been completed. **That's all part of the fun!**

For more SKIPS titles visit our website.

C O W

W

L

Have fun!

## SKIPS CHALLENGE TIME

Well done! Now copy the letters from the coloured tiles in the CrossWord into the matching coloured boxes below and **complete the sentence**.

**Remember:** boxes that are the same colour have the same letter in them.

 and

are wild cats.

Place a SKIPS CHALLENGE sticker here

*Well done! It's SKIPS sticker time.*

**35**

www.skipscrosswords.co.uk

# AROUND THE HOUSE

**All the answers below are from around the house.**

Fill in the missing letters and copy the whole word into the CrossWord puzzle as shown.

## ACROSS →   DOWN ↓

1)   b r u s h

2)  r u g

4)  p _ _

3)  s _ _ _ _

5)  kn _ _ _

4)  p l _ _ _

7)  t _ _ _ _

6)  f o _ _

9) 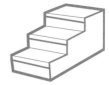 s _ a i r _

8)  b _ _ _

11)  c _ a i _

10)  s _ f _

If you are not sure of the answer, simply move on and revisit once a few clues have been completed. **That's all part of the fun!**

**36**

For more SKIPS titles visit our website.

Great job, keep going!

## SKIPS CHALLENGE TIME

Well done! Now copy the letters from the coloured tiles in the CrossWord into the matching coloured boxes below and complete the sentence.

Remember: boxes that are the same colour have the same letter in them.

Polly puts ☐☐☐☐ and ☐☐☐☐

in the pantry.

Place a SKIPS CHALLENGE sticker here

# WHO'S WHO?

**All the answers below are different occupations.**

Fill in the missing letters and copy the whole word into the CrossWord puzzle as shown.

## ACROSS →

1)  p i l o t

4) 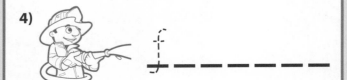 f _ _ _ _ _ _ _ _

5)  m _ n _ _ _ _

7) 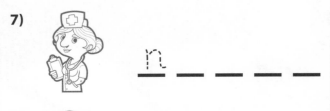 n _ _ _ _ _

8) 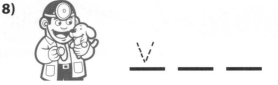 v _ _ _

9)  t _ _ ch _ _

## DOWN ↓

1) 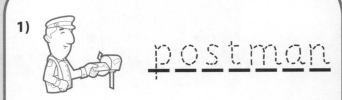 postman

2) 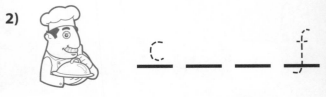 c _ _ f

3)  d _ _ ti _ _

4) 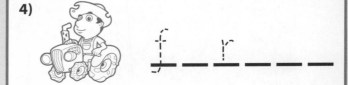 f _ r _ _ _

6)  d _ _ to _

If you are not sure of the answer, simply move on and revisit once a few clues have been completed. **That's all part of the fun!**

For more SKIPS titles visit our website.

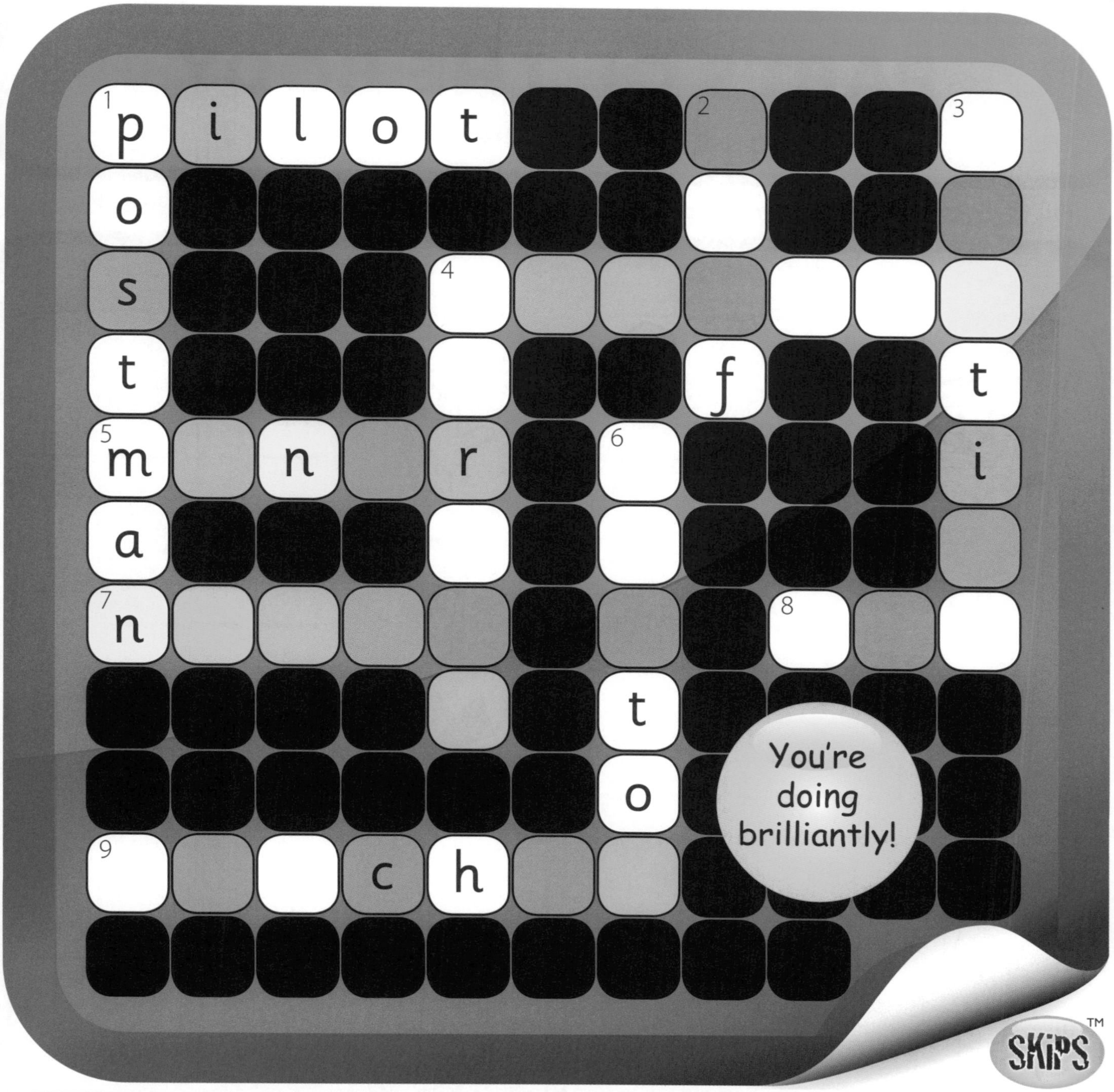
pilot
postman
You're doing brilliantly!
SKIPS

## SKIPS CHALLENGE TIME

**Well done!** Now copy the letters from the coloured tiles in the CrossWord into the matching coloured boxes below and **complete the sentence**.

**Remember:** boxes that are the same colour have the same letter in them.

Nine ☐☐☐☐ night

☐☐☐☐☐☐ nursing nicely.

Place a SKIPS CHALLENGE sticker here

*Well done! It's SKIPS sticker time.*

# PARTS OF THE BODY

**All the answers below are different parts of the body.**

Fill in the missing letters and copy the whole word into the CrossWord puzzle as shown.

## ACROSS →

1)  c h i n

4) k _ _ _

7) n _ _ _

8) a _ _

10) t _ _ _

13) t _ u _ _

14) t _ _ _ _ _

## DOWN ↓

2)  h a n d

3) e _ _

5) e _ _

6) f _ _ _

9) m _ _ _ _

11) e l _ _ _

12) n _ _ _

If you are not sure of the answer, simply move on and revisit once a few clues have been completed. **That's all part of the fun!**

For more SKIPS titles visit our website.

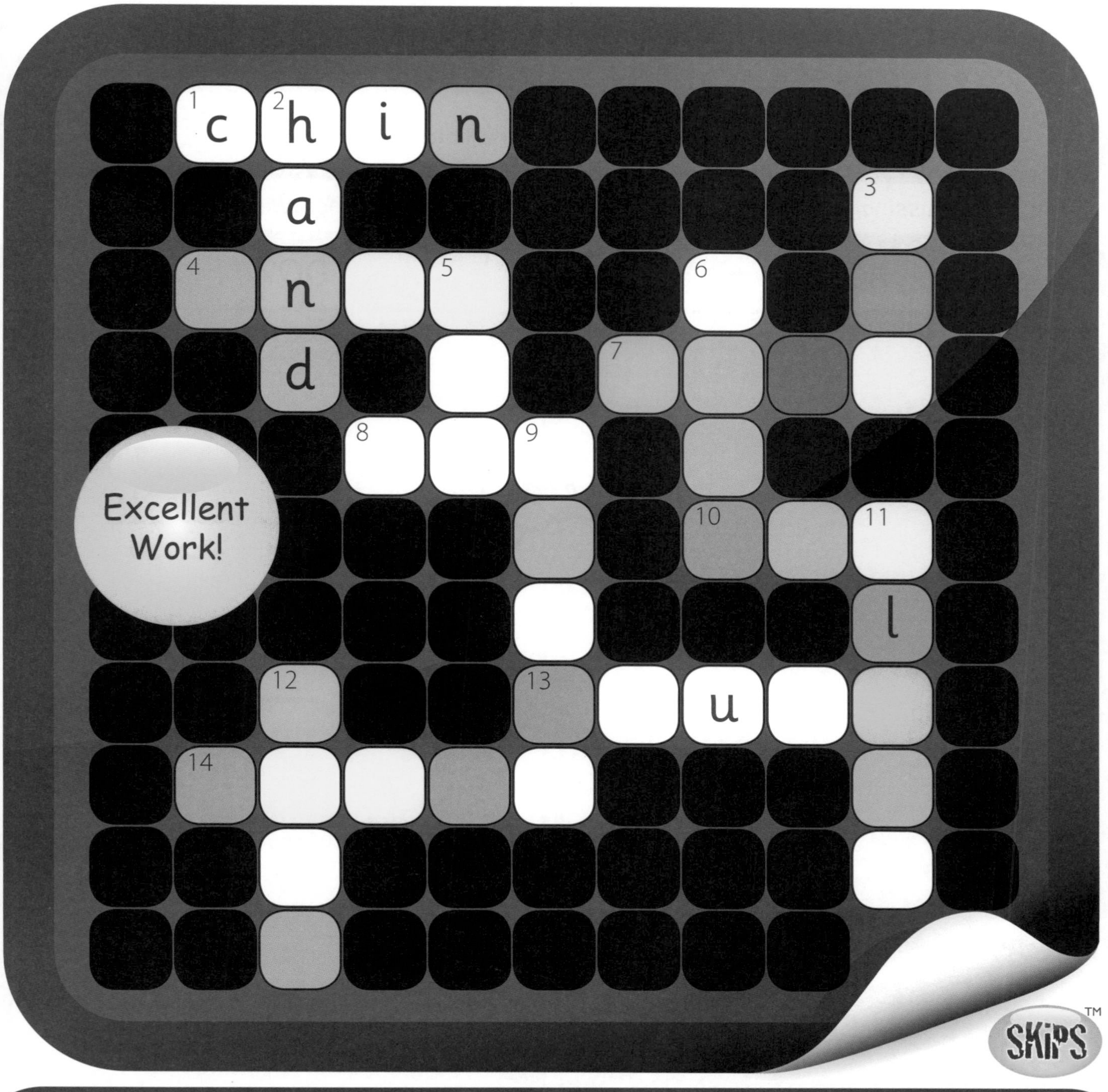


### *SKIPS CHALLENGE TIME*

**Well done!** Now copy the letters from the coloured tiles in the CrossWord into the matching coloured boxes below to **complete the joke**.

**Remember:** boxes that are the same colour have the same letter in them.

Q. Why didn't the [ ][ ][ ][ ][ ][ ][ ][ ] go to the party?

A. Because he had [ ][ ][ ][ ][ ][ ] to go with!

Take your book to school and ask your teacher to put a **WELL DONE SKIP!** sticker here, and there's another sticker for you.

*Great! Show your teacher how well you've done.*

# THINGS YOU DO (Verbs)

**All the answers below are things you do.**

Fill in the missing letters and copy the whole word into the CrossWord puzzle as shown.

## ACROSS →          DOWN ↓

1)  r e a d

2)  e a t

4)  r _ _ _

3)  d _ _

6)  s _ _

5)  d _ _ _ _

7) 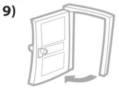 d _ _ _

6)  s m _ _ _

9)  o _ _ _ _

8)  r _ _ _

11)  b _ _ _ _

10) p _ _ _

For more SKIPS titles visit our website.

## SKIPS CHALLENGE TIME

**Well done!** Now copy the letters from the coloured tiles in the CrossWord into the matching coloured boxes below and **complete the sentence.**

**Remember:** boxes that are the same colour have the same letter in them.

Sleepy Wally ▢▢▢▢▢ into a ▢▢▢▢▢▢ door.

Place a SKIPS CHALLENGE sticker here

# CrossWord Practice 1

**Practice makes perfect!** **To get really good at something you need to practise.**

The numbers in the bracket at the end of each clue tells you how many letters are in the correct answer. The first ones have been done for you.

## ACROSS →

1) A yellow fruit (6)

3) The opposite of slow (4)

5) You bake cakes in this (4)

7) A sea creature with claws (4)

8) A baby sheep (4)

10) A person who bakes bread (5)

12) A spot (3)

14) The opposite of full (5)

## DOWN ↓

1) Something you read (4)

2) The month before Christmas (8)

4) To talk (5)

6) The opposite of white (5)

7) A young boy or girl (5)

9) A piece of furniture (5)

11) Feed (3)

13) The opposite of young (3)

If you are not sure of the answer, simply move on and revisit once a few clues have been completed. **That's all part of the fun!**

For more SKIPS titles visit our website.

## SKIPS CHALLENGE TIME

Well done! Now copy the letters from the coloured tiles in the CrossWord into the matching coloured boxes below to complete the joke.

Remember: boxes that are the same colour have the same letter in them.

Q. What did ⬜⬜⬜⬜ ⬜⬜⬜⬜ say

to mummy ⬜⬜⬜⬜ ?

A. Where's ⬜⬜⬜ corn?

Place a SKIPS CHALLENGE sticker here

Well done! It's SKIPS sticker time.

# CrossWord Practice 2

**Practice makes perfect!** **To get really good at something you need to practise.**

The numbers in the bracket at the end of each clue tells you how many letters are in the correct answer. The first ones have been done for you.

## ACROSS →

1) The opposite of blunt (5)

5) A key fits into this (4)

7) Big (5)

8) Enjoy (4)

11) A desert animal (5)

12) Part of the hand (5)

13) A male sheep (3)

14) A summer month (6)

## DOWN ↓

1) The opposite of whisper (5)

2) A person who flies a plane (5)

3) The month before May (5)

4) Talk (5)

6) A home for a dog (6)

9) Part of the arm (5)

10) Begin (5)

11) Which farmyard animal makes milk? (3)

*You're now ready to move up to the next SKIPS book.*

If you are not sure of the answer, simply move on and revisit once a few clues have been completed. **That's all part of the fun!**

This is the final puzzle! Well Done Skip!

**SKIPS**™

## SKIPS CHALLENGE TIME

Well done! Now copy the letters from the coloured tiles in the CrossWord into the matching coloured boxes below to **complete the joke**.

Remember: boxes that are the same colour have the same letter in them.

Q. Why ☐☐☐ ☐☐☐ ☐☐☐☐ tired?

A. It had been

 all day!

*Great! Show your teacher how well you've done.*

**47**

www.skipscrosswords.co.uk

# ANSWERS

Well done! Now check your answers and see how many questions you answered correctly.

Good luck!

## Page 4-5   Short Vowel Sound: "a"

| | ACROSS | | DOWN |
|---|---|---|---|
| 1 | bag | 1 | bat |
| 2 | tap | 3 | pan |
| 4 | fan | 5 | ant |
| 6 | cat | 6 | clap |
| 7 | crab | 8 | band |
| 10 | hand | 9 | lamp |
| 11 | pram | 10 | hat |

### SKIPS CHALLENGE

The fat (c)(a)(t) sat on a (r)(a)(t)

## Page 6-7   Short Vowel Sound: "e"

| | ACROSS | | DOWN |
|---|---|---|---|
| 1 | pen | 2 | net |
| 3 | wet | 3 | well |
| 5 | vet | 4 | tent |
| 6 | nest | 5 | vest |
| 8 | hen | 7 | ten |
| 9 | step | 10 | peg |
| 12 | leg | 11 | red |
| 13 | bed | 13 | bell |

### SKIPS CHALLENGE

Peg (l)(e)(g) fell in a (w)(e)(l)(l)

## Page 8-9   Short Vowel Sound: "i"

| | ACROSS | | DOWN |
|---|---|---|---|
| 1 | lip | 2 | pin |
| 3 | lid | 4 | dig |
| 5 | bin | 6 | ink |
| 7 | pig | 7 | pink |
| 9 | sink | 8 | fish |
| 10 | kick | 11 | king |
| 12 | ship | 12 | six |
| 14 | ring | 13 | kiss |

### SKIPS CHALLENGE

Thin as a (p)(i)(n) Jim wins a (b)(i)(n)

## Page 10-11   Short Vowel Sound: "o"

| | ACROSS | | DOWN |
|---|---|---|---|
| 2 | hop | 1 | box |
| 4 | fox | 3 | pot |
| 5 | cot | 4 | frog |
| 6 | dog | 5 | chop |
| 7 | spot | 6 | doll |
| 9 | lock | 7 | sock |
| 10 | log | 8 | top |

### SKIPS CHALLENGE

Is a (s)(p)(o)(t) a (d)(o)(t) or is a (d)(o)(t) a spot?

For more SKIPS titles visit our website.

## Page 12-13  Short Vowel Sound: "u"

| ACROSS | | DOWN | |
|---|---|---|---|
| 2 | bus | 1 | jug |
| 4 | gun | 2 | bun |
| 5 | nut | 3 | sun |
| 7 | drum | 6 | thumb |
| 8 | brush | 7 | duck |

*SKIPS CHALLENGE*

To eat a (b)(u)(n) in the (s)(u)(n) is fun!

## Page 14-15  Long Sounding: "a"

| ACROSS | | DOWN | |
|---|---|---|---|
| 1 | snake | 2 | nail |
| 3 | gate | 4 | train |
| 5 | cake | 7 | chain |
| 6 | lace | 8 | paint |
| 8 | plane | 9 | sail |
| 10 | tray | 10 | tail |

*SKIPS CHALLENGE*

If your name starts with "A" you can (s)(a)(y) "Hooray!"?

## Page 16-17  Long Sounding: "e"

| ACROSS | | DOWN | |
|---|---|---|---|
| 2 | sea | 1 | bee |
| 3 | eat | 2 | sheep |
| 5 | weak | 4 | tree |
| 7 | leaf | 6 | knee |
| 9 | pea | 8 | feet |
| 11 | key | 10 | three |

*SKIPS CHALLENGE*

If your name starts with "E" then (e)(a)(t) a (s)(w)(e)(e)(t)

## Page 18-19  Long Sounding: "i"

| ACROSS | | DOWN | |
|---|---|---|---|
| 2 | ride | 1 | night |
| 3 | bike | 2 | right |
| 4 | kite | 4 | knight |
| 5 | time | 8 | light |
| 6 | nine | 10 | fly |
| 7 | smile | | |
| 9 | knife | | |
| 11 | cry | | |

*SKIPS CHALLENGE*

If your name starts with "I" wink your (e)(y)(e)

## Page 20-21  Long Sounding: "o"

| ACROSS | | DOWN | |
|---|---|---|---|
| 2 | boat | 1 | yellow |
| 3 | loaf | 2 | blow |
| 4 | coat | 5 | tow |
| 6 | goat | 7 | rose |
| 9 | toast | 8 | bone |

*SKIPS CHALLENGE*

If your name starts with "O" touch your (t)(o)(e)

## Page 22-23  Long Sounding: "u"

| ACROSS | | DOWN | |
|---|---|---|---|
| 2 | music | 1 | tube |
| 4 | huge | 3 | chew |
| 5 | cube | 6 | uniform |
| 7 | unicorn | | |

*SKIPS CHALLENGE*

If your name starts with "U" say (w)(h)(o)(o)(o)(o)(o)(o) !

**49**

www.skipscrosswords.co.uk

## Page 24-25   Consonant Blends: "br"

| ACROSS | | DOWN | |
|---|---|---|---|
| 2 | brown | 1 | brick |
| 3 | brain | 2 | bread |
| 4 | break | 4 | bride |
| 6 | bridge | 5 | brush |
| 7 | brother | 6 | broom |

### SKIPS CHALLENGE

Brian (b)(r)(o)(k)(e) Brenda's (b)(r)(o)(w)(n) bracelet.

## Page 26-27   Consonant Blends: "ch"

| ACROSS | | DOWN | |
|---|---|---|---|
| 1 | chin | 1 | catch |
| 2 | chop | 3 | peach |
| 5 | chair | 4 | match |
| 7 | chain | 6 | witch |
| 9 | chick | 8 | torch |
| 10 | cheese | | |

### SKIPS CHALLENGE

Should Chester (c)(h)(o)(o)(s)(e) the shoes he (c)(h)(e)(w)(s) ?

## Page 28-29   Consonant Blends: "sh"

| ACROSS | | DOWN | |
|---|---|---|---|
| 2 | shoe | 1 | fish |
| 4 | ship | 3 | hush |
| 5 | shed | 6 | dish |
| 7 | shut | 8 | wish |
| 9 | sheep | 10 | push |
| 12 | shark | 11 | brush |
| 13 | shell | | |

### SKIPS CHALLENGE

Shelley sells (s)(h)(e)(l)(l)(s) on the (s)(e)(a)(s)(h)(o)(r)(e)

## Page 30-31   Consonant Blends: "st"

| ACROSS | | DOWN | |
|---|---|---|---|
| 4 | star | 1 | vest |
| 5 | stop | 2 | east |
| 6 | step | 3 | post |
| 7 | stick | 8 | chest |
| 11 | stairs | 9 | ghost |
| 12 | stamp | 10 | first |

### SKIPS CHALLENGE

Step by (s)(t)(e)(p) , let's go from (e)(a)(s)(t) to west.

## Page 32-33   Double Letters

| ACROSS | | DOWN | |
|---|---|---|---|
| 2 | feet | 1 | bell |
| 4 | heel | 2 | full |
| 5 | sleep | 3 | tall |
| 8 | loop | 6 | pull |
| 10 | stool | 7 | lorry |
| 11 | door | 9 | parrot |
| 12 | boot | | |

### SKIPS CHALLENGE

Silly (s)(h)(e)(e)(p) weep and (s)(l)(e)(e)(p)

## Page 34-35   Different Creatures

| ACROSS | | DOWN | |
|---|---|---|---|
| 1 | cow | 2 | owl |
| 3 | dog | 3 | duck |
| 5 | lion | 4 | goat |
| 6 | crab | 7 | bat |
| 8 | cat | 9 | ant |
| 11 | zebra | 10 | horse |

### SKIPS CHALLENGE

(t)(i)(g)(e)(r)(s) and (l)(i)(o)(n)(s) are wild cats.

For more SKIPS titles visit our website.

## Page 36-37　Around the House

| ACROSS | | DOWN | |
|---|---|---|---|
| 1 | brush | 2 | rug |
| 4 | peg | 3 | sink |
| 5 | knife | 4 | plate |
| 7 | table | 6 | fork |
| 9 | stairs | 8 | bath |
| 11 | chair | 10 | sofa |

**SKIPS CHALLENGE**

Polly puts 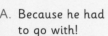 p o t s and
p a n s in the pantry.

## Page 38-39　Who's Who?

| ACROSS | | DOWN | |
|---|---|---|---|
| 1 | pilot | 1 | postman |
| 4 | fireman | 2 | chef |
| 5 | miner | 3 | dentist |
| 7 | nurse | 4 | farmer |
| 8 | vet | 6 | doctor |
| 9 | teacher | | |

**SKIPS CHALLENGE**

Nine n i c e night
n u r s e s nursing nicely.

## Page 40-41　Parts of the Body

| ACROSS | | DOWN | |
|---|---|---|---|
| 1 | chin | 2 | hand |
| 4 | knee | 3 | eye |
| 7 | nose | 5 | ear |
| 8 | arm | 6 | foot |
| 10 | toe | 9 | mouth |
| 13 | thumb | 11 | elbow |
| 14 | teeth | 12 | neck |

**SKIPS CHALLENGE**

Q. Why didn't the
go to the party?   s k e l e t o n

A. Because he had
to go with!   n o b o d y

## Page 42-43　Things You Do (Verbs)

| ACROSS | | DOWN | |
|---|---|---|---|
| 1 | read | 2 | eat |
| 4 | ride | 3 | dig |
| 6 | sit | 5 | dance |
| 7 | drink | 6 | smile |
| 9 | open | 8 | run |
| 11 | blow | 10 | pull |

**SKIPS CHALLENGE**

Sleepy Wally w a l k s into a
c l o s e d door.

## Page 44-45　CrossWord Practice 1

| ACROSS | | DOWN | |
|---|---|---|---|
| 1 | banana | 1 | book |
| 3 | fast | 2 | November |
| 5 | oven | 4 | speak |
| 7 | crab | 6 | black |
| 8 | lamb | 7 | child |
| 10 | baker | 9 | table |
| 12 | dot | 11 | eat |
| 14 | empty | 13 | old |

**SKIPS CHALLENGE**

Q. What did   b a b y   c o r n

say to mummy   c o r n ?

A. Where's   p o p   corn?

## Page 46- 47　CrossWord Practice 2

| ACROSS | | DOWN | |
|---|---|---|---|
| 1 | sharp | 1 | shout |
| 5 | lock | 2 | pilot |
| 7 | large | 3 | April |
| 8 | like | 4 | speak |
| 11 | camel | 6 | kennel |
| 12 | thumb | 9 | elbow |
| 13 | ram | 10 | start |
| 14 | August | 11 | cow |

**SKIPS CHALLENGE**

Q. Why   w a s   t h e   n o s e
tired?

A. It had been   r u n n i n g   all day!

# ORDER FORM

| TITLE | | RRP |
|---|---|---|
| **SKIPS KS1 CrossWord Puzzles**<br>Key Stage 1 English | ISBN 978-0-9567526-5-9 | £7.99 |
| **SKIPS KS1 CrossMaths Puzzles**<br>Key Stage 1 Maths | ISBN 978-0-9567526-4-2 | £7.99 |
| **SKIPS KS2 CrossWord Puzzles**<br>Key Stage 2 English Book 1 | ISBN 978-0-9567526-6-6 | £7.99 |
| **SKIPS KS2 CrossWord Puzzles**<br>Key Stage 2 English Book 2 | ISBN 978-0-9567526-2-8 | £7.99 |
| **SKIPS KS2 CrossMaths Puzzles**<br>Key Stage 2 Maths Book 1 | ISBN 978-0-9567526-7-3 | £7.99 |
| **SKIPS KS2 CrossMaths Puzzles**<br>Key Stage 2 Maths Book 2 | ISBN 978-0-9567526-3-5 | £7.99 |
| **SKIPS 11+ CrossWord Puzzles**<br>11 Plus English | ISBN 978-0-9567526-0-4 | £9.99 |
| **SKIPS 11+ CrossMaths Puzzles**<br>11 Plus Maths | ISBN 978-0-9567526-1-1 | £9.99 |

## Teachers and Tutors

You will be eligible for discounts on purchases of sets of 10 copies or more. Further details are on our website. An on-line order form is also available.

**You can order our books by post or email or purchase directly from our website.**

 sales@skipscrosswords.co.uk

 www.skipscrosswords.co.uk

 SKIPS Crosswords
142 Newton Road, Great Barr
Birmingham  B43 6BT
United Kingdom

For more SKIPS titles visit our website.

SKiPS
SKiPS
SKiPS
SKiPS
SKiPS
SKiPS
SKiPS
SKiPS
SKiPS
SKiPS
SKiPS
SKiPS
SKiPS
SKiPS
SKiPS
SKiPS
SKiPS
SKiPS
SKiPS
SKiPS
SKiPS
SKiPS
SKiPS
SKiPS

Skips Challenge stickers

Well Done SKiP!

Well Done SKiP!

Well Done SKiP!

Well Done SKiP!

Well Done SKiP!

Well Done SKiP!

Well Done SKiP!

Well Done SKiP!

Well Done SKiP!

Well Done SKiP!

**Well Done Skip! Stickers**